B

C000091042

FOUR SEASONS POETRY BOOKS

SPRING

COMPILED BY JENNIFER WILSON

ILLUSTRATED BY GRAHAM COOPER

Macdonald Children's Books

Contents

Introduction

An artist with a paintbrush or camera can often make us look in a new way at something which we know very well. Poets can also use their skill with words so that we look at everyday things with new interest. Have you ever thought of Chinese characters when you see television aerials on roof tops, or the sea as a hungry dog, or butterflies as flying flowers? Sometimes poets invite us to imagine the world from other points of view. Celandines catch light. A rainbow holds out a shining hand. Putting words together which we do not usually hear together or turning things back to front can also lead to new thoughts about old things. Have you ever made a jigsaw puddle or noticed an invisible drone booming by with a beetle in it?

We sometimes get impatient in Spring when Winter will not let go. These poems may enliven some things which we want to wish away to get on with Summer. And there is a touch of madness, as mad as a March hare.

Jennifer Wilson

By the Canal, Early March

The snow is trash now and the blackbirds sing
A gold and blue day trying to be Spring.
A gray sludge fringes the canal where swans,
Almost as gray, surge by, their wings like tents,
Hissing with love between the tenements.

Posters are peeled that once hung in the air
Their vulgar summers; but drab windows stare
Winking and blinking at the boisterous sun.
Low, the brown water breaks in glass and high
The tall mill cracks its smokelash in the sky.

And everything is headlong, rushing through
Spaces of sun and sky, their gold and blue,
Towards that still certain time when buds all break
And sparrows quarrel in the dust and men
Lounge their ways home and swans are white again.

Norman MacCaig

Do You Call it Happy?

Do you call it happy –
When the sun shines through the rain
and the droplets on the new pink leaves
catch the light again?

Do you call it beautiful –
the scent that's on the bank
from bluebells and the bugle flowers
and mosses dark and damp?

Do you call it spring again –
When midges start to bite
and blackbirds find a singing bough
and celandines catch light?

Laurence Smith

I Meant to Do My Work Today

I meant to do my work today –
But a brown bird sang in the apple tree,
And a butterfly flitted across the field,
And all the leaves were calling me.

And the wind went sighing over the land
Tossing the grasses to and fro,
And a rainbow held out its shining hand –
So what could I do but laugh and go?

Richard le Gallienne

Blue-Butterfly Day

It is blue-butterfly day here in spring,
And with these sky-flakes down in flurry on flurry
There is more unmixed colour on the wing
Than flowers will show for days unless they hurry.

But these are flowers that fly and all but sing:
And now from having ridden out desire
They lie closed over in the wind and cling
Where wheels have freshly sliced the April mire.

Robert Frost

7

Astronomer

On a lone hillside
A Navajo shepherd
Wrapt in his blanket,
Hugged his knees,
Dreamed into the night –
A wisp of crescent,
A sky full of stars –
In his thought
He was asking:
"Do my lanterns
Shine up to the stars?"

David O'Neil

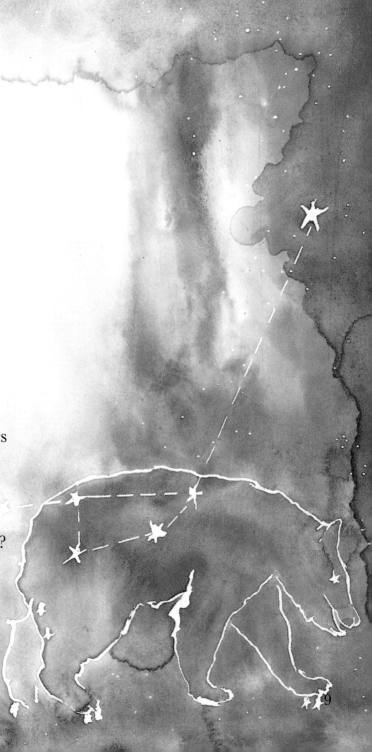

Questions at Night

Why
Is the sky?

What starts the thunder overhead?
Who makes the crashing noise?
Are the angels falling out of bed?
Are they breaking all their toys?

Why does the sun go down so soon?
Why do the night-clouds crawl
Hungrily up to the new-laid moon
And swallow it, shell and all?

If there's a Bear among the stars,
As all the people say,
Won't he jump over those pasture-bars
And drink up the Milky Way?

Does every star that happens to fall
Turn into a firefly?
Can't it ever get back to Heaven at all?
And why
Is the sky?

Louis Untermeyer

Spring

When daisies pied, and violets blue,
And lady-smocks all silver-white,
And cuckoo-buds of yellow hue
Do paint the meadows with delight,
And cuckoo then on every tree
Sings cuckoo, cuckoo.

William Shakespeare
from Love's Labour's Lost

Feeding Ducks

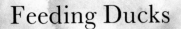

One duck stood on my toes.
The others made watery rushes after bread
Thrown by my momentary hand; instead,
She stood duck-still and got far more than those.

An invisible drone boomed by
With a beetle in it; the neighbour's yearning bull
Bugled across five fields. And an evening full
Of other evenings quietly began to die.

And my everlasting hand
Dropped on my hypocrite duck her grace of bread.
And I thought, 'The first to be fattened, the first to be dead',
Till my gestures enlarged, wide over the darkening land.

Norman MacCaig

11

The Sea

The sea is a hungry dog,
Giant and grey.
He rolls on the beach all day.
With his clashing teeth and shaggy jaws
Hour upon hour he gnaws
The rumbling, tumbling stones,
And 'Bones, bones, bones, bones!'
The giant sea-dog moans,
Licking his greasy paws.

And when the night wind roars
And the moon rocks in the stormy cloud,
He bounds to his feet and snuffs and sniffs,
Shaking his wet sides over the cliffs,
And howls and hollos long and loud.

But on quiet days in May or June,
When even the grasses on the dune
Play no more their reedy tune,
With his head between his paws
He lies on the sandy shores,
So quiet, so quiet, he scarcely snores.

James Reeves

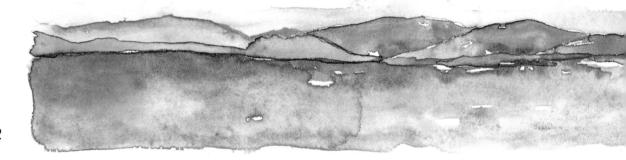

Sea Fever

I must down to the seas again, to the lonely sea and the sky,
And all I ask is a tall ship and a star to steer her by,
And the wheel's kick and the wind's song and the white sail's
    shaking,
And a grey mist on the sea's face, and grey dawn breaking.

I must down to the seas again, for the call of the running tide
Is a wild call and a clear call that may not be denied;
And all I ask is a windy day with the white clouds flying,
And the flung spray and the blown spume, and the sea-gulls
    crying.

I must down to the seas again, to the vagrant gypsy life,
To the gull's way and the whale's way where the wind's like a
    whetted knife;
And all I ask is a merry yarn from a laughing fellow-rover,
And quiet sleep and a sweet dream when the long trick's over.

John Masefield

Very Curious

I am in the dog house,
yesterday in the soup,
tomorrow I may be over the moon
or, perhaps, a silly goose.

Am I the apple of father's eye
and sometimes bold as brass
as I lead him in a merry dance
and then go up in smoke?

Will mother give me a black look,
fed up to her back teeth
for she crosses my palm with silver
and has a heart of gold?

So what does it all mean
for I am as green as green,
if all of it were really true,
then who am I, and who are you?

Leonard Clark

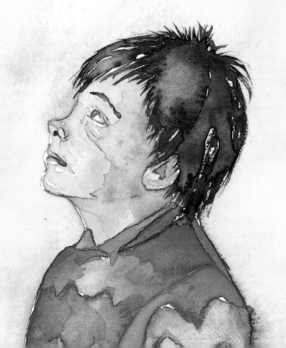

There Was a Young Lady Whose Chin

There was a Young Lady whose chin
Resembled the point of a pin:
So she had it made sharp,
And purchased a harp,
And played several tunes with her chin.

Edward Lear

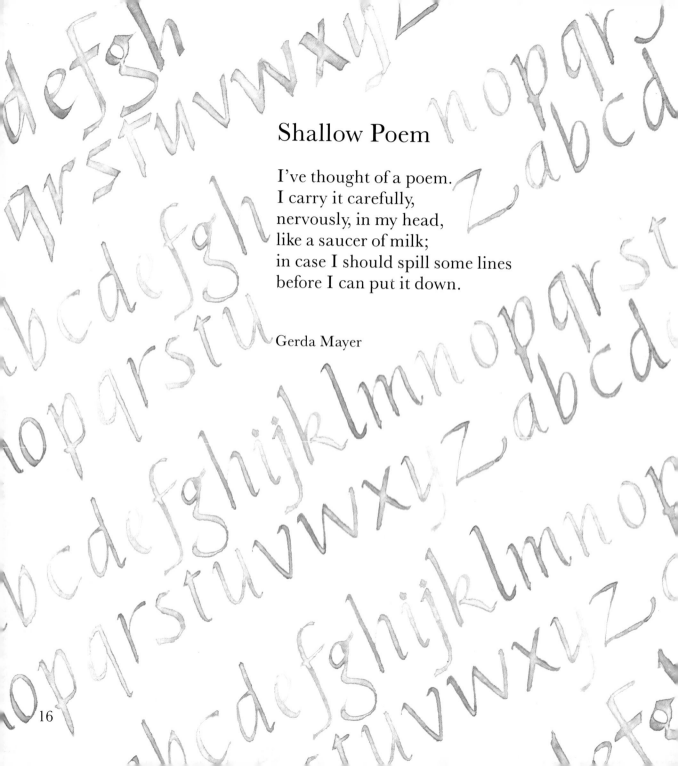

Shallow Poem

I've thought of a poem.
I carry it carefully,
nervously, in my head,
like a saucer of milk;
in case I should spill some lines
before I can put it down.

Gerda Mayer

16

Old Poet

The alder tree
shrivelled by the salt wind
has lived so long
it has carried and sheltered
its own weight
of nests.

Norman MacCaig

17

The Mud

This glistening mud that loves a gate
Was mashed by cows of late,
But now its puddles lie so still
They hold the clouds and trees and hill;
But when the painted cows come out
From milking-shed to grass
And churn the mud up as they pass,
How cloud and tree and hill will dart about!

Andrew Young

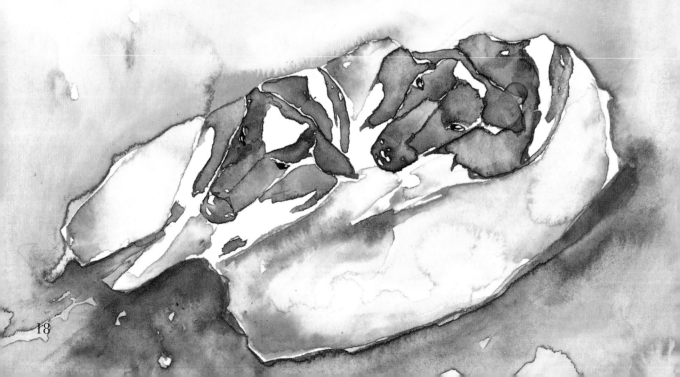

Jigsaw Puddle

Sloshing my boat in the pavement puddle
I jiggle the sky above,
I fold the clouds in a sheep-like huddle,
I bobble the sun in the blue and white muddle –
And then I stand still –
Till the jigsaw puddle
Is smooth as a mirror again.

Emily Hearn

Tall Nettles

Tall nettles cover up, as they have done
These many springs, the rusty harrow, the plough
Long worn out, and the roller made of stone:
Only the elm butt tops the nettles now.

This corner of the farmyard I like most:
As well as any bloom upon a flower
I like the dust on the nettles, never lost
Except to prove the sweetness of a shower.

Edward Thomas

On Roofs of Terry Street

Television aerials, Chinese characters
In the lower sky, wave gently in the smoke.

Nest-building sparrows peck at moss,
Urban flora and fauna, soft, unscrupulous.

Rain drying on the slates shines sometimes.
A builder is repairing someone's leaking roof,

He kneels upright to rest his back,
His trowel catches the light and becomes precious.

Douglas Dunn

Caterpillar

He stands on the suckers under his tail,
stretches forward and puts down
his six legs. Then he brings up
the sucker under his tail, making
a beautiful loop.

That's his way of walking. He makes
a row of upside-down U's
along the rib of a leaf. He is as green
as it.

The ways of walking! – horse, camel,
snail, me, crab, rabbit –
all inventing a way of journeying
till they become like the green caterpillar
that now stands on his tail
on the very tip of the leaf and sways, sways
like a tiny charmed snake,
groping in empty space for a foothold
where none is, where there is no
foothold at all.

Norman MacCaig

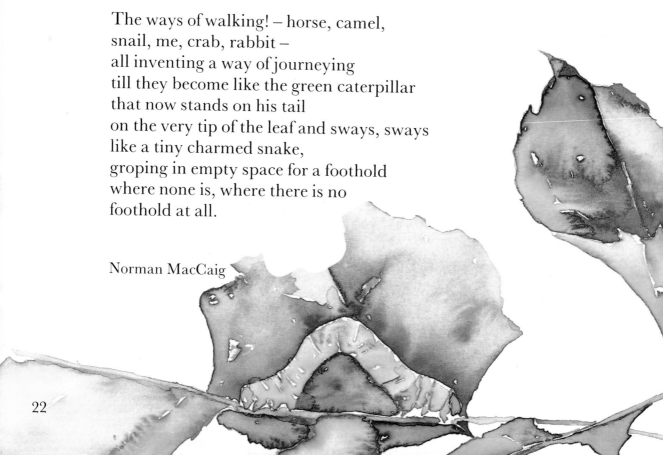

To a Squirrel at Kyle-Na-No

Come play with me;
Why should you run
Through the shaking tree
As though I'd a gun
To strike you dead?
When all I would do
Is to scratch your head
And let you go.

W.B. Yeats

The Panther

The panther is like a leopard,
Except it hasn't been peppered.
Should you behold a panther crouch,
Prepare to say Ouch.
Better yet, if called by a panther,
Don't anther.

Ogden Nash

The Termite

Some primal termite knocked on wood
And tasted it, and found it good,
And that is why your Cousin May
Fell through the parlor floor today.

Ogden Nash

Lodged

The rain to the wind said,
'You push and I'll pelt.'
They so smote the garden bed
That the flowers actually knelt,
And lay lodged – though not dead.
I know how the flowers felt.

Robert Frost

26

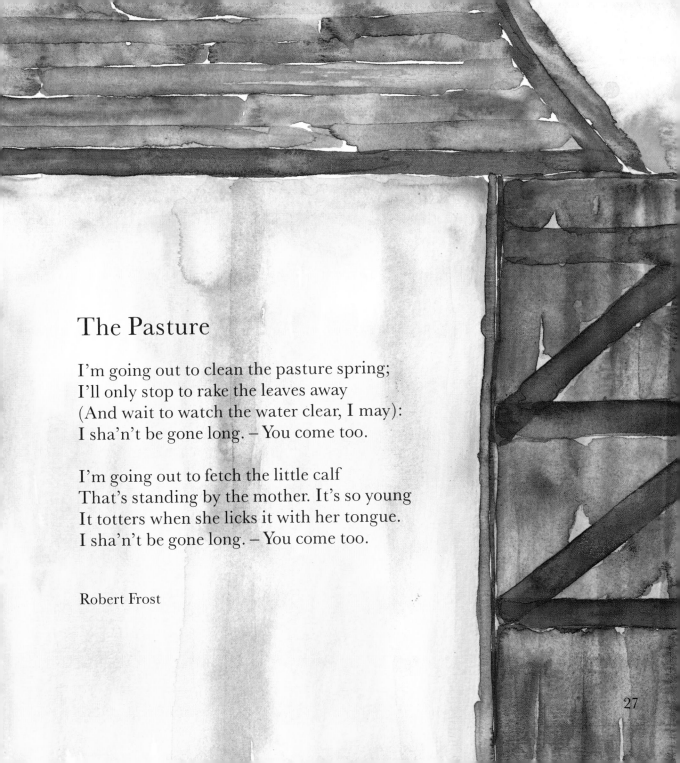

The Pasture

I'm going out to clean the pasture spring;
I'll only stop to rake the leaves away
(And wait to watch the water clear, I may):
I sha'n't be gone long. – You come too.

I'm going out to fetch the little calf
That's standing by the mother. It's so young
It totters when she licks it with her tongue.
I sha'n't be gone long. – You come too.

Robert Frost

Today Was Not

Today was not
very warm
not very cold
not very dry
not very wet.

No one round here
went to the moon
or launched a ship
or danced in the street.

No one won a great race
or a big fight.

The crowds weren't out
the bands didn't play.

There were no flags no songs
no cakes no drums.
I didn't see any processions.
No one gave a speech.

Everyone thought today was ordinary,
busy busy
in out in
hum drummer day
dinner hurry
grind away day.

Nobody knows that today
was the most special day
that has ever ever been.

Ranzo, Reuben Ranzo,
who a week and a year ago was gone
lost
straying starving
under a bus? in the canal?
(the fireman didn't know)
was here, back,
sitting on the step
with his old tongue lolling,
his old eyes blinking.

I tell you –
I was so happy
So happy I tell you
I could have grown a tail –
and wagged it.

Michael Rosen

There Was a Roaring in the Wind All Night

There was a roaring in the wind all night;
The rain came heavily and fell in floods;
But now the sun is rising calm and bright;
The birds are singing in the distant woods;
Over his own sweet voice the Stock-dove broods;
The Jay makes answer as the Magpie chatters;
And all the air is filled with pleasant noise of waters.

All things that love the sun are out of doors;
The sky rejoices in the morning's birth;
The grass is bright with rain-drops; – on the moors
The hare is running races in her mirth;
And with her feet she from the plashy earth
Raises a mist; that, glittering in the sun,
Runs with her all the way, wherever she doth run.

William Wordsworth
from Resolution and Independence

Weathers

This is the weather the cuckoo likes,
  And so do I;
When showers betumble the chestnut spikes,
  And nestlings fly:
And the little brown nightingale bills his best,
And they sit outside at 'The Travellers' Rest,'
And maids come forth sprig-muslin drest,
And citizens dream of the south and west,
  And so do I.

This is the weather the shepherd shuns,
  And so do I;
When beeches drip in browns and duns,
  And thresh, and ply;
And hill-hid tides throb, throe on throe,
And meadow rivulets overflow,
And drops on gate-bars hang in a row,
And rooks in families homeward go,
  And so do I.

Thomas Hardy

Acknowledgements

Culford Books wish to thank the following for their kind permission to use their material:

'Very Curious' Leonard Clark from THE CORN GROWING Hodder & Stoughton Ltd.'On Roofs of Terry Street' Douglas Dunn from TERRY STREET Faber & Faber Ltd. 'Blue-Butterfly Day', 'Lodged', 'The Pasture' from THE POETRY OF ROBERT FROST edited by Edward Connery Lathem, Jonathan Cape Ltd reprinted by permission of the Estate of Robert Frost and Copyright © 1969 by Holt, Rinehart and Winston, Inc. Copyright © 1962 by Robert Frost. Copyright © 1975 by Lesley Frost Ballantine. Reprinted by permission of Henry Holt and Company Inc. 'Jigsaw Puddle' © Emily Hearn. 'I Meant to Do My Work Today' Richard le Gallienne from POETS CORNER edited by Barbara Ireson Nelson by permission of The Society of Authors as the literary representative of the Estate of Richard le Gallienne. 'By the Canal, Early March', 'Caterpillar', 'Feeding the Ducks' 'Old Poet' Norman MacCaig from COLLECTED POEMS by Norman MacCaig Chatto & Windus Ltd. 'Sea Fever' John Masefield by permission of The Society of Authors as the literary representative of the Estate of John Masefield. 'Shallow Poem' Gerda Mayer from THE KNOCKABOUT SHOW Chatto & Windus Ltd. 'The Panther', 'The Termite' Ogden Nash from I WOULDN'T HAVE MISSED IT (1977) Andre Deutsch Ltd. 'Astronomer' © David O'Neil. 'The Sea' James Reeves © James Reeves Estate. Reprinted by permission of The James Reeves Estate. 'Today Was Not' Michael Rosen from 'WOULDN'T YOU LIKE TO KNOW (1983) Andre Deutsch Ltd. 'Do You Call It Happy' Laurence Smith from CATCH THE LIGHT: poems by Laurence Smith, Gregory Harrison, and Vernon Scannell (1982) Oxford University Press. 'Questions at Night' from RAINBOW IN THE SKY by Louis Untermeyer. Copyright 1935 by Harcourt Brace Jovanovich, Inc., Renewed 1963 by Louis Untermeyer. Reprinted by permission of the Publisher. 'To a Squirrel at Kyle-na-no' W. B. Yeats by permission of A. P. Watt Ltd., Michael B. Yeats and Macmillan London Ltd. 'The Mud' Andrew Young from THE POETICAL WORKS OF ANDREW YOUNG Martin Secker & Warburg Ltd.

Every effort has been made to trace copyright holders, but in two cases this has proved impossible. Culford Books apologize for these unwilling cases of copyright transgression and would like to hear from the copyright holders not acknowledged.

A MACDONALD CHILDREN'S BOOK

This collection of poetry © Jennifer Wilson 1987
Introduction © Jennifer Wilson 1987
Illustration © Graham Cooper 1987
FOUR SEASONS POETRY BOOKS © Culford Books 1987

First published in Great Britain in 1987 by
Macdonald & Company (Publishers) Ltd
This edition Macdonald Children's Books
Simon & Schuster International Group
Reprinted 1989
All rights reserved

Conceived, edited, designed and produced by Culford Books,
Sunningwell House, Sunningwell, Abingdon,
Oxfordshire OX13 6RD
Edited by Penelope Miller
Designed by Judith Allan
Photoset by Lantern Graphics Ltd

Printed and bound in Great Britain by
BPCC Paulton Books Limited

Macdonald Children's Books
Simon & Schuster International Group
Wolsey House, Wolsey Road,
Hemel Hempstead HP2 4SS

British Library Cataloguing in Publication Data

Spring. —— (Four seasons poetry).
    1. Spring ——Juvenile poetry 2. Children's
poetry, English
    I. Wilson, Jennifer II. Cooper, Graham
III. Series
821'.008'033   PZ8.3

ISBN 0-7500-0039-2